Please, Puppy, Please

by Spike Lee & Tonya Lewis Lee

illustrations by Kadir Nelson

SCHOLASTIC INC.
New York   Toronto   London   Auckland   Sydney
Mexico City   New Delhi   Hong Kong   Buenos Aires

Stay inside today,
puppy puppy, please, puppy.

Outside? Let's go play,
puppy, puppy, puppy, please.

Away from the gate,
puppy puppy,
please, puppy.

Oh wait, **puppy**, wait, please, pl**ea**se, please, **please.**

Come back here! Don't go,

puppy puppy, **please**, puppy.

Not the mud, puppy. Oh no,
puppy, puppy, puppy,
please.

Rub-a-dub-dub,
please, please,
puppy puppy?

Get back in the tub,

Puppy puppy puppy,

please!

Watch out for the cat,
puppy, please, puppy,
please!

Oh no, don't do that,
puppy puppy,
please, puppy!

Fetch me the ball,
puppy, puppy, puppy, please!

Come when I call,
puppy, please, please, please,
please!